Fawn Eyes

Written by Jean Sakamura

Illustrated by Hala Day

Fawn eyes see blue sky.

Fawn eyes see tall grass.

Fawn eyes see a butterfly in the sun.

What do your eyes see?

Fawn ears hear soft wind.

Fawn ears hear a cricket chirp.

Fawn ears hear the buzz of wild bees.

What do your ears hear?

A fawn nose smells damp earth.

A fawn nose smells white flowers.

A fawn nose smells where a rabbit hopped.

What does your nose smell?

Fawn feet run in cool shadows.

Fawn feet run in warm sunlight.

Fawn feet run in soft summer grass.

Where do your feet run?